A Horse

By

Michael Ellis

Contents

Chapter One

Dawn of a New Life

Somewhere I heard that when one life is over, another one begins. This is my story. My humans named me Espirit da Chavel, which means "Spirit of the Horse." To all my human and animal friends, I'm called Spirit. I was named after my father. His name is Espirit, which in French means "Spirit." Espirit was the Stallion of the barn where I lived. A stallion is a male horse; most humans only keep the fastest and strongest ones bred to their female horses called mares. Espirit had been the father to many of the babies in the barn. In horse language, baby horses are called foals. What a sight he was to behold with his wavy black mane streaked with strands of blond hair, jet black tail, and two white socks on his front legs. His body was the color of a bright new copper penny with a black stripe down his back. With his broad chest and strong muscles, all the mares in the barn admire him. When I grow up, I will take his place as Stallion of the barn!

The day was August 20, 1997, and it was sunny and hot with a slight breeze out of the North. That morning the owners of a gray mare named Missy, who lived at the barn, had to have their dog Sammy put to sleep. Sammy was an old golden retriever that stayed at the barn when her owners were away. His muzzle had changed from its golden color to dull grey. He was having difficulty getting around the barn. The local animal doctor called a Vet for short; he had come to the barn that morning and told Sammy's owners that it was time for him to leave this place for a better one, a place without pain where he could run and jump with others. It was a typical hot summer afternoon in Georgia. Many of the barn boarders had come for Sammy's funeral, including my future owners. As one of the humans walked back from the funeral, he stopped to check on my mother, who would have a baby. That same Vet had told my owners earlier that I wasn't going to be born for another three weeks. But as the human was watching my mother, he knew something would happen. It was time for me to make my appearance.

He started to call out for other humans to help him. Everyone was racing around trying to clean the special birthing stall. This was a special stall with high walls and a camera placed inside so the barn owner could watch the mother horses having babies. If a mare started to have problems, the owners could see the situation and rush to the stall to help her.

The prior occupant had left it a mess, so it had to be cleaned to make a comfortable bed for my mother to lie in while I was being born. Brittany, whose mother owned the barn, ran for fresh wood shavings. Humans were rushing around removing the old shavings, and Brittany was depositing the new shavings in the stall. Brittany ran into the big house for the camcorder yelling back at the other humans that she wanted to videotape my birth. A human brought out a lead rope and moved my mom from her stall into the clean birthing stall with its smell of fresh-cut pine wood shavings.

I was born at 7:45 p.m. that day. Everyone was around my mother and me. Gone were the sad looks on everyone's face from Sammy's funeral. All wanted to see the new arrival. My mom's name is Stormy, and she is a registered Quarter Horse. She has white hair with black skin giving her a bluish appearance. I would be my mother's first and only baby. The barn owner, Gini, was standing by in case the mother needed any additional help.

The first thing I remember seeing was a German Shepard named Toby and an Australian Shepherd whose name was Callie; they greeted me by licking my face. They would be my friends and guardians, and I would spend many a day running and playing with them growing up.

Unfortunately, my first attempt to stand was a disaster. My long legs wobbled, and I started to bounce off the stall wall, and down I fell. Callie was terribly upset, thinking I was going to hurt myself. Finally, I could stand up on my hooves after the fourth attempt. I was standing but not particularly good my legs were still shaky, and I bumped into everything. Oops, sorry, mom, I didn't mean to bump into you. Copper and Callie both found it challenging to stay out of my way, so I didn't step on them.

After a few minutes, I got the hang of it and was doing a surprisingly good job of walking around and inspecting everything.

There were a lot of humans hovering around our stall. Several were sitting on top of the stall walls. Mother leaned over and whispered in my ear in a low voice, "the two humans standing by the stall door are our owners. My female owner is June, and the male owner is Mike. The other female human standing next to June is Gini; she owns the barn."

By this time, I was starving. My instincts told me I needed to get some of my mothers' milk into me, or I would die. Her milk has medicine in it that I must have in the first several hours to help me build up tolerances to many diseases. I was having difficulty locating the right spot to nurse. Gini and June tried to move me to the right direction, but I resisted. They called the veterinarian to see how long I could go without nursing. Gini relayed to my owners what the vet had said. I could only go three hours without nursing. If I didn't nurse, they would need to rush me to Auburn, Alabama that has a special horse hospital to be bottle-fed. Without either my mothers' milk or special bottle-feeding, I would die.

Finally, after what seemed an eternity, I found the right spot on my mother. Warm milk ran down my throat. It made me feel so good and warm all over. My mother was exhausted after everything that had happened that afternoon. She lay down on the floor of the stall to rest. After a few minutes, I decided I was also exhausted and could fold my long spindly legs, and down onto the ground I fell; not very graceful, I might say. But I was able to be next to my mother. While I was next to her, Copper and

Callie came and lay down next to us. I was so tired that just after a few moments, my eyes started to get heavy, and in a few minutes, I was lying flat on the ground. I was in a deep sleep. Thoughts of tomorrow were running through my mind, and I was sure it would be a day full of excitement.

Chapter Two

My First Day of Stable Life

Morning came early with the roosters in the barn waking us up with their crowing. The loudest of them was called Hank. He ruled the rest of the roosters and hens with his strong will and sharp spurs on his legs. Hank started crowing first; then the others joined in. My mother was already awake and was standing over me, looking around the barn. My father was on the other side of the aisle that ran down the middle of the barn. Mama could barely see him from our stall.

I stretched my front legs out first and then my back legs. I arched my back and tightened my back muscles. It felt so good to stretch out my whole body lying on the floor of our stall. Then placing my front feet out, I braced myself and stood up. I certainly was a lot more graceful this time than yesterday. Walking around my stall, I was greeted by Rainbow and Priss, the two barn cats. Both were standing on the top boards of my stall, looking down at me. Rainbow was a gray tiger with a wisp of white on her tail, and Priss was solid black with yellow eyes. I went over to them, reached up with my head, and sniffed them. They smelled quite different from Mama or even Copper or Callie, and in a flash, both cats made a hissing sound at me and ran across the tops of the other stalls to the other end of the barn.

I looked across the aisle into the stall across from ours and saw another horse looking back at me. Mama told me the other horse was another stallion named Rambo, who was only two and a half years old. He was a golden palomino, and even at his young age, Rambo was already as tall as my father.

"Hey, squirt," someone said. I looked up, and next to our stall, through the wood slats, I could see a beautiful big black horse with just a touch of brown around his nose. He had a black mane and a long black flowing tail. "My name's Thunder, and I'm a Tennessee Walker. Your mother and I belong to the same human family. My humans' name is Mike while your mothers' human is June, and you and I are going to be best buddies." Your Dad might be the Stallion of the barn, but I'm the top horse around here. When I say stop, everyone listens. Stick with me, kid, and I will show you." "**Thunder!**" mother stopped him in the middle of his sentence; "your head is getting so big with all you're boasting; soon, you're not going to be able to get out of your stall door."

Thunder Again
Front of Barn

Soon I could hear a lot of noise coming from one end of the barn. A group of humans was leading horses out of their stalls; some horses were in the center of the barn, while others were located on the sides of the barn. Several horses passed in front of our stall.

Mama was introducing them to me. First was Skippy, a brown horse with a wavy brown mane. He had a white stripe running up his right front leg, stopping at his knee. "Why is Skippy so large around the middle of his stomach," I asked? Skippy stopped and gave me a stern look. The human leading him pulled on the lead rope and told him to keep walking.

Mama explained that Skippy was what the humans call an easy keeper, which meant that he would put weight on even with only a tiny amount of food. The humans had put Skippy on a diet to help him lose those extra pounds, and he wasn't happy about it. Yesterday, when the little girl who owned him was riding in the arena, he bucked and tossed her off his back. She landed hard, and several humans ran over to check out. One of the older humans checked her out and said, "The little girl had a few bumps and looks like she was going to be OK. The arena's ground was very sandy and cushioned her fall. The only thing she hurt was her pride." The next morning when she came to the barn, she had small bruises on her leg and hip. Everyone said she was a fortunate girl. This was the first time Skippy had ever done something like this. The little girl's father was terribly angry and said they would have to sell him if he did it again. He would not take the risk of having Skippy hurt his daughter.

Behind Skippy was a big horse; he was primarily black with some white on his body. Mother said they call his coloring paint, and his name was Cowboy. His mane

15

was mostly white, with black highlights streaked throughout it. He also had a white star on his chest. His face was all white. What caught my attention were his eyes. Each eye was a different color. One was steel blue, and the other was dark brown. When he looked at me with that blue eye, I felt he could see straight through me.

He was very tall. Mama said, "Cowboy was almost 17 hands". I asked her what she meant by hands, and she explained that humans use hands to tell how tall a horse is. Four inches equals one hand so, four times 17 is equal to 68 inches tall.

While talking about him, his owner had taken him out of his stall to ride. It was an amusing sight because he was so tall, and his female owner was so short and chubby that she had to stand on a big box to get on him. The big problem was Cowboy wouldn't stand still for her. His owner would get on the box, and he would start to move forward enough so his owner would about fall onto the ground. This happened several times until finally, a male human walking by stopped. He grabbed the reins and held him still. Cowboys' owner thanked the other human and scolded him for being such a bad horse. Standing on the box again, the owner swung her large leg over the saddle, and with a big push on her bottom by another human, she landed on top of him. Cowboy gave a massive sigh as his owners' weight landed on his back. She straightened herself up while the other human let go of the reins. This caused the human's hat to fall to the ground. The other human went over and picked the hat up, handed it to her, and told her that she needed to work harder on Cowboy's ground manners. Whatever that was, I guess sometime later in my life; I would find out what ground manners were.

Everything was so interesting on my first day. I learned about several of our neighbors, but now I was hungry and more interested in feeding my stomach. Mother could sense my needs, and with her head, she nuzzled me over to her, and I started to nurse.

It was difficult to understand what my mother was trying to say with my stomach full. My eyes were so heavy I lay down on the stall floor. The heavy scent of pinewood shavings surrounded me. Sleep was not far away, but finally, I could understand what mama was trying to tell me. "Sleep, my son, because tomorrow will be another exciting day."

Chapter Three

Danger at the Barn

I woke up to a high pitch noise near the barn. Something was chasing the chickens around the yard. It gave me such a scare that I jumped to my feet. I looked around; everything was pitch black. The only sign of light was at a house across from the barn. It took a few minutes for my eyes to adjust to the darkness. There was just enough light coming from the house porch light that I could see mama. She was staring out into the darkness, with her ears pointing forward and smelling the air. I could tell she had spotted something outside. "What is it," I asked; she was still watching whatever it was and told me to be very still and quiet, not to move.

Several of the chickens were flying into the barn and landed in the rafters over Cowboy's stall. Suddenly one of the chickens outside gave a large squawk, and then it was quiet again. "Mama, what's going on?" I asked again. She turned around, walked toward me, and lowered her head this time.

"Coyotes," she said, "sometimes they come late at night to try and catch something to eat. They look like a dog, about the size of Callie, with a round and bushy tail. Coyotes are light gray or tan with a black tip on the tail. They are getting very brave coming so close to where the humans live. Walk over by the door and smell the air." I did what she said. I could smell something strange in the air. It was extraordinarily strong and pungent. It made me snort, and I shook my head. I was trying to get the smell out of my nose. "What is it," I asked?

"It's their scent. Remember tonight and remember that smell. Usually, they will not try and come into the barn. But when we are out in the pasture at night, and you are standing watch, remembering tonight and their smell could save us from a coyote attack."

Tonight, one of the chickens was not as lucky as the others. Most of them usually sleep up in the barn's rafters for protection, but tonight several decided to venture out in search of small bugs to eat. Usually, Hank, the rooster, would go with them for protection. He would use the large sharp spurs on his legs as weapons to strike at his enemies, trying to cut them. This would usually keep the coyotes away from his chickens. This time they went out without him.

"Mama, what did you mean by standing watch?" "Spirit, just go back to sleep; you have much to learn." My eyes started to feel so heavy that they felt soothing and warm when I closed them. Sleep had overcome my body, but something inside me had changed. I realized another world was outside my little birthing stall as I slept.

I was very restless that night and had difficulty sleeping. Images of coyotes and chickens running around were haunting me. Every sound startled me. A screech arose from the pasture and a swooping sound in the grass. I jumped to my feet and looked around. "Mama, what's that," I asked?

"Spirit, that's a bird, it's called a hawk, and he probably caught a field mouse out in the pasture." She said they hunt both at night and during the day. "Everything is OK. You can go back to sleep," she said.

In a low, gruff voice, I heard someone in the stall across from us. It was Cowboy. "Be quiet; some of us need to get some sleep; our owners will be here early tomorrow

to ride us. I will need all my strength to carry her. So, go
back to sleep."

Chapter Four

Baby Feeding Time

I had images of the coyotes running through our barn with last night's excitement. It made it difficult to go back to sleep. This time I could not lie down. Mother suggested I try and get some rest standing up. "You will need your rest because tomorrow will probably be another big day," she said.

Morning came very quickly. As usual, Hank the rooster let out a big crow. Rise and shine, he was saying. It is time for everyone to get up.

Several owners started to show up, and the barn began to come alive with many humans running around. I could hear Cowboy and the others stomping their feet on the ground. Even my mother was pacing up and down the front of our stall. What's going on? I asked? She explained that everyone was getting excited with anticipation of being fed breakfast. I could hear Cowboy let out a big whinny; I'm starved; he said, "Feed me first."

Peeking out between the boards, I could see the middle of the barn. Two humans were walking down the aisle. Each had a stack of buckets in their arms. They were stopping in front of each stall. One of the humans would set the stack on the ground, pick out a bucket and empty the feed into another bucket mounted in the corner of the stall. I could hear several of the horses kicking at their stalls. Skippy was trying to jump over the top board of his stall, trying to bite at Cowboy next to him. One of the humans yelled, "Get down, Skippy, and stop it; your food is coming." Skippy was telling Cowboy to watch out that this food belonged to him, and he wasn't going to share it.

The more I watched, the more I could feel my stomach rumbling. Hunger was setting in, so walking by my mother, I stuck my head under her and began nursing. Again, warm milk was going down my throat and filling my stomach. Mother started to pace again. She was moving around so much that it was impossible to nurse.

Finally, one of the humans filled our food buckets. Mother dove her head into her bucket and started to eat. Then the human put a small amount of food in a special bucket next to my mother. He told me this was special food just for me. I was watching mother eat. The food had an extremely sweet smell, so I decided to try some. I walked over to the bucket and saw small bars over the top of it.

There was just enough space between these bars that I could get my small head between them to eat. It was hard, and sweet not like my mother's milk. I had to chew it several times before I could swallow it. After a few more times of trying the feed, I decided it was surprisingly good. Mothers' milk was still the best.

After several minutes of eating, I soon lost interest in this hard food and went back to nursing. I didn't have to work as hard with that. I dove and pushed my head under my mother to try and reach her milk sack to start nursing. Suddenly, I felt my mother bite me on my butt. Ouch, that hurt. I jumped back and swung my head around to see her. A stern look in her eye quickly told me not to be so rough. I understood what she was telling me, but my butt hurt for several minutes afterward. This time when I went to nurse on her, I lowered my head and softly nuzzled at her. I could feel her relax and soon felt her sweet, warm milk start to fill my stomach.

After several minutes of nursing, Mother decided she wanted to try and eat some of my food out of the special bucket, but her head was way too wide to fit between the bars. She kept trying to squeeze her mouth between them. I could see the bars starting to bend, but not enough to allow her to reach any of my food. After several attempts, she finally gave up and went back and finished her food.

Chapter Five

The Trail Ride

The first human that came back into the barn was the owner, Gini, and I could hear her talking to other humans following her. She told them that there was a trail ride scheduled in an hour there would be seven people with one riding double; she then started to name several horses that needed to be saddled and ready to go. "Don't forget to brush Thunder," the owner told another human. Mike should be here shortly to load him, and he will be leading the ride. I also need two other riders to go along. "Kathy, will you and Cowboy be able to go? Tony, will you and Skippy bring up the end of the ride?"

"Mother, what's is a trail ride"? She explained that the farm was large, and she heard several humans talking a long time ago that the rides helped pay for the barn. They were usually during the weekends except in the summertime when the days are long. Strangers would come out to ride several of the horses from the barn into the woods. The barn assigned horses to the experience level of the strangers. The trail was about 10 miles long and would take about an hour. We would ride over bridges, through water, up and downhill's. All the horses would follow each other nose to tail with an experienced rider and guide horse at the front and another experienced rider and horse at the end. On some of the trail rides, when there were a lot of inexperienced riders, Gini would place an added experienced rider in the middle to prevent any accidents.

Most horses did not try to hurt anyone on these trail rides; in fact, we loved going out on the trail. It's just after several trail rides; we got so bored and would make it a little difficult for the rider to control us. If we had a real inexperienced human rider, we would drop our heads to eat grass or leaves along the ride. This would pull reins out of the riders' hands and scare the humans. Sometimes we would walk off the regular trail and make our own through the woods. We would even try to pass other horses on the ride. This was usually not a good idea because it would usually result in getting other horses upset and even kicking each other. Usually, we would start to act up when we were tired of being ridden at the end of the day.

Mama said she felt sorry for Thunder many times because he usually had to be a lead horse for these trail rides.

He would take out between three to five rides a day every weekend.

I stuck my head through the wood slats into Thunder's stall. I asked him if he got tired of doing trail rides. Thunder's head rose high in his stall, and his chest swelled with pride, and he said, "No, both my owner Mike and I feel proud that we are providing a service which is rarely offered anymore. Mike told me that there are very few places for other humans to enjoy the outdoors while sitting on the back of a horse. In the old days, we were the main way humans could get around, but with the invention of automobiles, we were replaced and rarely used except for pleasure."

He told me a story about a trail ride they had taken out last summer, long before I was born. It was a scorching day, and a group of Girl Scout Brownies had come for a trail ride. The sky was overcast. I heard Mike talking and told the other humans the weather forecast did not call for any rain, so it should be a good ride.

There were around eight Girl Scout Brownies; most girls were around ten years old and had never ridden a horse. We were taking the lead, and Cowboy was in the middle, and a new horse to the barn named Apache was bringing up the end.

Halfway through the ride, the wind picked up, getting dark. Then the rain came. It rained so hard and lightning and heavy winds. The trees were swaying back and forth that I thought they would blow over at times. Many branches were falling around us. Mike and I maneuvered the other horses under a couple of enormous trees for shelter. We were too far to go back to the barn and too far to complete the ride. So, we had to wait for the storm out under the trees. I was so scared, but don't tell your mother or any other horse in the barn. I knew I could not show my fear because the other horses would also panic and try to run, causing a disaster, and many of the riders would get hurt. The girls were crying and wanted to go back, but my human Mike "told them we were safer to wait for the storm out here under these huge trees. I think his soothing voice is what helped me settle down and kept me from being scared.

After about 15 minutes, the storm had passed, and the sun creeped out behind the clouds. We headed back to the trail and completed the rest of the ride. Coming down the hill towards the barn, we could see several humans cheering. Everyone was happy to see that no one had been hurt. Mike told the humans how excellent I was and kept all the other horses calm during the storm.

Mother said, "**Thunder,** that's enough of the stories; it's late, and Spirit needs his rest; there will be plenty of time to tell more stories.

Chapter Six

Mothers' Story

Mother then told me her owner June occasionally would ride her on large or difficult trail rides. Most of the weekends, she was used as a lesson horse, helping with small young humans called children teaching them how to ride. Mother said she remembers one time she was working with a little boy child whom June told her was handicapped.

The boy was laughing and giggling when he was on her back; both June and Gini were walking on each side of her. They were holding onto the little boy so he would not fall off. After the lesson, June told her that she was extremely proud of her and that the little boy had a great time. "You've come a long way from the frightened horse we purchased," June said. Mother said that this was one of the finest lessons she had ever given.

In the evenings, before the sun would go down, Mother and June would go for a quiet ride on the trail, just the two of them. Mother said June would tell her this was their bonding time, then leaning over the saddle, she would give her a big hug around the neck. June's voice had a slight quiver, and Mother felt moisture dripping on her neck. She could tell that June had been crying, and the tears would drop on her. Neither of us understood what bonding meant, but Mother said that when June would talk to her with her soothing tone of voice, she was finally feeling safe and secure. With June's actions, Mother knew she was loved.

Mother told me she was originally born in Platte City, Missouri, on July 09, 1986. She had moved a total of five times before coming to the barn. Much of her prior experiences with humans were memories of cruelty.

One

owner had beaten her so severely that they had broken a couple of her teeth. So, she did not like being around humans until June purchased her from the barn. She was kind and understanding and would talk to her very softly. Even when she would be awfully bad and act up on the trails, she would still be very understanding.

June was like a protector to my mother. She told me about the time the Ferrier was cleaning and trimming her hooves. I asked her if it hurt having her feet cleaned. She said, "Not when June does it, but sometimes I have problems when the horse Ferrier does it." Usually, we must have our feet trimmed every six to eight weeks. If we don't have it done, the front part of our hoof, called the toe, can get long and cause us walking problems. She then told me about an evil Ferrier the barn used to use.

His name was Fred. Once Fred was trimming her hoof, he put her leg between his legs to trim it. A strange feeling swept over her; she had to run away but couldn't because her leg was trapped. She had gotten so scared and panicked. She pulled and pulled and finally managed to pull her leg free. Then she spun around. Fred was lying in a heap on the ground. When mother had pulled her leg free of his hold, it caused him to lose his balance and sent Fred flying into the air and falling about five feet away. His face was bright red, and he was furious. Mother said she heard Fred say, "No darn horse is going to do that to me. I'll teach you a lesson you'll never forget". Then he reached into his toolbox and came out with a large metal rasp. With all his might, he hit her across her nose with that rasp. June returned to see if Fred was finished. There was a trail ride waiting to go out, and Mother was scheduled to lead it. She looked at Mother and saw the blood streaming down mothers' nose. When she saw what he had done, she started to yell at him. Hysteria set in, and the screaming got louder. June repeatedly told him that he was fired and that she would tell Gini. Mother said, "this is how I got this big scar on my nose." Mother said Fred was never seen again at the barn.

With this new home and a new owner gone forever were the beatings. Instead, June replaced it with kisses and apples. I started to love and trust June more and more. Mother told me if she had one wish, she hoped I would have an owner that would be just like her, kind and loving.

Chapter Seven

Pasture Life

When I woke up today, at first, it seemed like any other day. The barn owner and my owners were feeding all the horses in the barn. Other humans arrived and were grooming their horses and cleaning their hooves. Mama said this is what humans called our feet. It seems kind of silly to me why they don't just call them feet, but that's humans for you. Many of them were standing by our stall and looking at me. Suddenly I had a feeling something special was going to happen today.

I could hear them talking that today would be a big day as he would be introduced to the pasture. Mother, what are they talking about? Since I was her first baby, she said she wasn't sure what they meant. When June finished helping feed everyone, she and Mike came by our stall. June opened the stall door and came in. She started to brush my mother and then cleaned her hooves. First, June picked up a tool called a hoof pick, cleaned her front foot, then reached down picked up her back foot cleaning it. She then went around to her other side and did the same.

Finally, June was done with my mother, looked at me, and said, "Next." She moved towards me and said she would make me very handsome, whatever that meant. She brushed me all over and combed out my short mane. She moved her hands up and down my legs. I looked at mom; what is she doing. Mother said June was probably getting me used to having my legs handled. I sure felt like one of the big guys now. I sure wish I had a long-flowing mane like my fathers. Mother told me this would come when I get older. Then June put what she called a halter on Mother and attached a lead rope to it. Mike opened the door, and June walked with Mother out of the stall. June asked Mike, "do you think I need to put a halter on Spirit." He told her not to worry that I would follow my mother, and he was right; as soon as she was in the main aisle of the barn, just out of my sight, I started to worry. Looking around our stall, I had mixed emotions; curious to see what great adventure was ahead for us today, but also afraid to leave the safety of my birthing stall.

So, in a flash, I ran and caught up to them. As I walked next to them, I noticed most of the stalls were empty. Mother, I wonder where everyone is? She looked down at me and told me everyone must be out in the big pasture.

"Spirit, it looks like you're going to meet the entire herd for the first time," she said.

After a couple of minutes, we walked out into the daylight, and across from the barn, there was a wide-open space mother called "the pasture." June and Mike lead mother through the gate, which was the entrance to the pasture. I quickly followed them. Several other humans were standing by the fence, watching us as I looked around.

June removed mothers' halter and told her to have fun and not get into trouble. It had been several weeks since she could run free and graze on fresh grass. I was standing by the entrance looking at the humans. When I turned around, mother was already in the middle of the pasture. I started to panic ran after her. I hadn't gotten but a few feet into the pasture when I was stopped in my tracks by several of the horses from the barn. Many of them I had never seen before. I recognized Cowboy, then there was Skippy, and behind them was Thunder. Before I knew it, I was surrounded by six other horses. I was extremely nervous, but I was also terrified. I wasn't sure what they wanted. I decided the best way to find out what they wanted was to introduce myself. Hi, my name is Spirit. I would tell them more about me but was cut short by one of them.

We know, your Stormy's baby. My name is Nikki, and this is Gideon, that's Arizona, and behind you, the big one is Jessie, then there's Vision and Rocky. We saw you coming out to the pasture and wanted to see you. Our stalls are at the other end of the barn so that we could smell you in the barn, but we wanted to see who everyone had been talking about. Rocky here used to be the baby of the barn, but it looks like that spot belongs to you now. Rocky was smaller than the other horses. He had a brown body and legs with a dark brown mane, tail, and legs. His body was very lean and muscular. I learned he was a breed originally from

Spain called Paso Fino. "Hey kid," Rocky said, "you are going to love living here." Thanks, I replied. I really love my mother, and so far, everyone I've met has been great. Rocky told me the barn was exciting with something going on most weekends. I'd love to stay and chat with you, but right now, I need to catch up with my mother and see what she's doing. With a burst of speed, I left Rocky behind me.

As I ran to catch her, I passed several other horses. It was a wonderful feeling, my lungs filling up with warm summer air and the muscles in my legs and hindquarter feeling so powerful. Later I would learn everyone's name not only by sight but also their smell. I sure did love this feeling of the wind, sun, and all the pasture smells. A sweet smell stopped me in my tracks. Mother, what's that smell; it's coming from those pretty white flowers on that vine. Spirit, that's wild honeysuckle; its fragrance can be smelled throughout the pasture this time of the year.

I could see at the fence line the faces of several of the humans starting to lead us back to the barn. It was a great day of adventures and meeting new friends. I'm sure there will be many more of these times, and I will look forward to them all.

Chapter Eight

Walk in the Woods with Mother

June was one of the first humans that came out, snapped a lead rope to the ring on mothers' halter, and led her back to the barn. Of course, I followed right next to her; I would not let her get out of my sight; we went straight up the center of the barn and into our stall. She started to brush mother again. I heard June tell my mother that she could not see how she could get that dirty in such a short time.

This time June started to use a curry brush on her back, side, and behind her front legs. Then she followed up with a soft brush removing all the hair loosened from the curry brush. Hanging on the wall of our stall was a large brown object. "Mother, what's that?" She told me that it's called a saddle which the humans put on our back and sit on. Those long pieces hanging down have what's called stirrups at the end, which they put their boots into. The big knob on the top is called the horn. Some riders hold onto it to help keep them in the saddle. So, it looks like we were going for a trail ride.

As I peeked through the slats of our stall, I could see Thunder was getting the same treatment as Mother. Then June yelled to Mike to see if he was done with Thunder. "Yes, I'm just finishing putting his bridle on." I looked at Mother, and she told me it was like the halter we wear but with a metal bar called a bit which goes into our mouth. This helps humans turn our head, and where our head goes, our body must follow. She sometimes said the bit tastes funny. Some humans don't put the bridle on correctly. The bit hits the back of our front teeth and hurts. In the winter, it gets really cold and feels like ice in our mouths.

June and Mike know the importance of the bridle and always put it on Thunder and me precisely right, so we don't have any problems.

Then Mike asked June what she was going to do with me. She replied that she didn't think I would be a problem. Where Stormy goes, I'm sure Spirit will follow. She started to lead my mother out of the stall, and June was correct; there was no way I was going to let my mother out of my sight.

We went out the backside of the barn. June was on Mother's left, and suddenly they stopped. She placed her left boot into the stirrup, grabbed the horn, and swung her right leg over mother and the saddle. In a flash, she was sitting on top of her. I couldn't believe it. I had never seen anyone on top of her. I walked up and started to chew on June's boot. Basically, I was trying to tell her I didn't like this. Mother then told me it was OK, and June leaned over, patted me on top of my head, and said it was OK also.

They started to walk away from the barn up a hill toward the trees. This was great! I never knew this side of the barn even existed. As I looked around at all the sites, I noticed a clump of grass. I started to eat it when I raised my head; next to my mother was Thunder. Then several other horses joined them. I recognized the horses but not the riders. There was Jessie, Arizona, Cowboy, and Skippy.

June called to Mike, "where do you want Stormy?" "Put her at the end," Mike said. she then laid the reins on Mother's neck. She turned in a half-circle and went to the back of the line closer to where I was eating. I went over to see if she was OK. Before I could ask, Mike yelled to everyone, "head um up and move um out."

Chapter Nine

My First Trail Ride

Thunder was the first to move up the hill. Skippy followed behind Thunder, then Jessie, and Arizona. Cowboy had to trot to catch up, but he quickly moved up behind Arizona with his long legs. Then mother moved up behind Cowboy. I had to run to catch up, but I moved next to her after a couple of long strides. We quickly entered the woods. It was cool and damp on the trail. Much of it was still wet from the rain the night before. Everyone was walking in a single line, head to tail. In some spots, the trail was narrow, so narrow that sometimes it was difficult to walk next to mother. The trail had a lot of twists and turns.

Then, the trail opened at one point, and ahead I saw a wooden bridge. I could see it crossed over a small little creek. Thunder was, of course, the first; he pranced across like it was nothing.

Then everyone followed but Cowboy. Cowboy stopped at the edge of the bridge. I could see him looking to the left then to the right trying to find a way from not having to cross the bridge. His rider was experienced dealing with his minor problems, so she tapped her heels on Cowboy's sides. Cowboy responded by putting first his right hoof on the wooden portion of the bridge. Then his left foot, and soon he bolted across the bridge. It caught her by surprise. I could see she almost was tossed off, but she grabbed hold of the saddle horn and up pulled herself back into the saddle.

Mother looked over at me; then June said, "let's show Cowboy how it's done," and we both trotted across the bridge. When we got to the other side of the bridge, I stopped for a second and wondered why Cowboy made such a big deal of it. I looked down into the water. It was exciting staring down into the water. The trail ride had already made its way up a small hill when I looked up. I ran and quickly caught up to mother when I heard Mike yell over his shoulder, "we're coming up to the bird trail; see how many birds you can find." As I looked around, I saw what looked like wooden birds on various trees. One rider called out, "I see one on a tree to my right." After a few minutes, it seemed like each rider saw the birds. Mike yelled, "that there were eight birds, so keep your eyes open for three more." Several more of the riders spotted another two, but they never did find all eight."

We rounded a bend. There were two giant trees, one on each side of the trail. After we went between them, the trail opened to a large grassy area. As soon as we got into the pasture, Cowboy stopped, his head went down, and he started to eat some of the luscious grass. His rider started to yell and gave a hard pull on the reins. I think it surprised him because he jerked his head up, and he had this weird

47

look on his face. At the same time, I enjoyed the lush green grass when I looked up the trail ride had moved almost across the field then stopped at the bottom of a hill.

Mike gave out a giant yell, "Yee Ha, this is Giddy Up Hill. See everyone at the top." In a flash, both Mike and Thunder took off at a gallop and raced up the steep hill on the trail. Everyone quickly followed at the same speed. I could tell it looked like everyone was having fun, so I followed. I was right; it was great to stretch my legs and kick dirt up with my hoofs. We raced around the curves and twists on this part of the trail. I almost passed mother at one spot in the trail, but suddenly the trail took a sharp turn, and I started to slide. My one back foot slid out from underneath me. I could feel myself going down but decided the others would not see me fall. I slowed up enough, which allowed me to catch my balance and prevent a disaster. Just then, I saw Mother fly past me. We finally reached the top of the hill and in front of us was a huge pasture, and at the back end of it, there it was the barn, home.

Chapter Ten

First Trim Job

Days turned into weeks and weeks into months. Thunder was staying in the barn for most of the trail rides. Mother and June had been taking out most of them. We had not seen Mike for several weeks, then this weekend, they both showed up. Mike and June both were in our stall talking. She asked how the classes were going, and Mike told her different stories about the Ferrier classes he was taking.

I looked over at mother, and she explained that Mike was learning to be a horse Ferrier, and that's why we had not seen him around the barn. He probably is here to trim our hooves. Mike left our stall while June put our halters on us.

She was right, as usual. I could see Mike walking over to his truck. He reached into the back and came out with a wooden box full of tools and a metal stand. Mother, I'm not so sure about this. June went into Thunders' stall. Mike then joined June in Thunder's stall first. She asked him if she needed to put his halter on, but

Mike said, "it won't be necessary Thunder won't move." I peeked through the slants and saw Mike put the wooden box down in the sawdust. He had a pair of short leather pants over this shoulder. Later, Mother said these were called "chaps." He swept the chaps around the back of his waist and buckled them. Then pulled them around and repositioned them to his front; he bent over and hooked each leg, first his right, then left. He was facing Thunders hind end, picked up his right hoof, and brought it up between his legs.

He reached into a pouch in the chaps and pulled out a hoof pick. Cleaning out Thunders hoof, he went into another pouch, pulled out a knife, and started to work the bottom of his hoof. He then reached into the wood box and brought out a metal tool, and proceeded to trim his hoof. Thunder was excellent and never moved. He then put the tool back into the box and retrieved another. This was a flat tool called a rasp used to smooth the bottom of the hoof. Mike moved the hoof and stretched it out front of Thunder and onto the stand in a flash. He turned around and used the same tool to smooth the edge of the hoof. I couldn't see, but he did the same with the other three hooves. By this time, Mike was really sweating. When he was done, he leaned against the stall wall and yelled to June that Thunder was done, and we were next.

I looked over at Mother, and she tried to reassure me that everything would be OK. Mike opened our stall door in a few moments, and both walked in. "Which patient is next" Mike asked June. "What about doing Spirit then, Stormy" June replied. Mike still had his chaps on and walked over towards me. I wasn't afraid of him but wasn't sure of having my feet done.

June hooked a lead rope to my halter and brushed me with my soft brush. Mike started by talking to me, telling me everything would be OK. He first picked up my right foot and patted the bottom of it with his hoof pick. I thought it seemed like a regular cleaning that June had done many times before. Then Mike put my hoof between his legs, same as he did with Thunder, and started to file the bottom of it. That was it! I felt like I had to run but couldn't. I was trapped, and the only thing I could think of was flight. I needed to getaway. I started to pull away from the lead rope hooked to my halter, which June held tightly. She kept talking to me, trying to get me to calm down, but I could feel the tension flow from her through the rope into me. It was just feeding my need to get away. I pulled and started to rear up. The next thing I knew, I had pulled my hoof out from between Mike's legs and leaped over him. He tucked down and rolled around the sawdust in the stall.

By this time, I was so scared, thinking I had done something so terrible the only thing I could do was standstill, I lifted my tail, and a massive release of gas exploded from my butt. The sound was heard throughout the barn. Both Mike and June stopped what they were doing, covered their noses, and started to laugh uncontrollably. June was the first to speak, "Spirit was that you; it's, it's awful; like a terrible smelling fog hanging over the stall" then they looked at each other, and both started to laugh again.

Mike said he thought that was enough excitement for one day and proceeded to redirect his farrier talents on Mother.

It would be several weeks before he tried to trim my hoofs again. This time I would have a better idea of what to expect, so I decided to follow Thunders' example and standstill. To this day, everyone in the barn is still talking about my unique physical ability.

Chapter Eleven

The Weaning

This day seemed like any other day at the barn. Mike and June showed up early and were brushing Mother and Thunder. When they were done, both came into my stall and brushed me. I was so excited because I thought we were going out on a trail ride again.

June was asking Mike if he thought Stormy would be OK over there. She said she had come so far in trusting us I didn't want to hurt her. I wasn't sure what they were talking about, but by the tone of their voice, I could tell they were sad; gone was my feeling of excitement. I asked Mother if she had any idea what they were talking about. She said no; she had no idea but felt we would soon find out. June kept talking to me, telling me I would be fine. "Thunder will watch over you and guide you. Oh, and your buddy Rocky will also be there to help."

All the time she talked to me, she continued to brush me. Then suddenly, she did something I had never seen her do, she started to cry. Mike walked over to her, put his arms around her, and told her everything would be OK, and he loved her.

I could see Mother was getting very restless and was stirring around in the stall. What's wrong, I ask. Mother said she had an idea what they were talking about, and she didn't like it. She started pawing at the floor of the stall. I began to get restless myself.

June left me to try and settle Mother down while Mike stayed with me. Finally, we both settled down after a few minutes, but I could still tell Mother was upset. Soon more of the owners showed up. I could tell something was up. Usually, they went straight to their horses to get them brushed and saddled for riding. Instead, everyone gathered around our stalls.

Mike left me and started to walk down the barn's center aisle toward the opening. I stuck my head over the stall door and watched him walk away. At the end of the barn, I could see Gini standing by the horse trailer with the back open. The gate was down, and at first, I thought a new horse was arriving. I stuck my head out as far over the door as it would reach, but I couldn't see anyone in the trailer.

June was putting Mother's halter on her, then she hooked a lead rope to it, opened the stall door, and led her out. At the same time, two of the other humans who kept their horses at the barn came into the stall. I had seen them many times before. One of them owned Rocky, and the other helped at the barn. They both told me everything would be OK, but I could tell this was not true.

I leaned over the door just as far as I could. Even the wood started to crack because of my weight pushing against it. I could see June and Mother going down the center aisle toward the trailer. At first, I just gave Mother a whinny to tell her I was coming. Then as they got closer to the opening of the trailer, Mother turned her head back toward me and gave out a loud cry.

Several other humans helped her load Stormy on the trailer, but it wasn't easy. She made it very clear she did not want to get in it. Two male humans finally stood on each side of her butt, locked their hands, and with a mighty heave pushed on her, and she finally put one hoof on the edge of the trailer, then another, and then stepped up into the trailer. Mike quickly closed the trailer's back gate behind her.

At that moment, both of us knew what was going on. I could hear Mother's voice yelling for me. Her voice was echoing throughout the barn. I also screamed back, telling her that I didn't want her to go. I reared back and put my front feet on top of the door and was going to try and climb over, but the humans pulled me back.

I heard the truck pull away. I rushed to the other side of my stall, which faced the outside of the barn. I could see the truck and the trailer Mother was in pull away. I continued to yell and could hear Mother screaming back. My heart was breaking, and I could not imagine having her close to me. What was I going to do?

Then I heard a voice from the stall next to mine; it was Thunders. He told me every young horse goes through this, called weaning. He said your heart would hurt for some time, but it will pass. The yearning for her milk will go away. Have trust in our owners June and Mike; they are doing the right thing for both of you. I'm not sure where they are taking her, but she will be safe and well cared for. When it's time, she will return.

Then I heard Rocky from across the aisle. Spirit he called; I just went through weaning last year. They probably are taking her to another farm not too far from here. My mother told me all about it. It's a beautiful place with a huge pasture, plenty of green grass, and plenty of fresh water, and only one or two other horses are there. Gini takes several of the herd there twice a year for a big trail ride. Remember, Thunder, you and Stormy have gone there several times. Thunder thought for a second and said he remembered it; yes, it's called Broken Arrow Farm.

I gave one more whinny for Mother, but there was no reply. After hearing what Thunder and Rocky told me, I started to feel a little better. I stood there looking out in the direction the truck and trailer had gone but couldn't see anything, just the road, and trees. I didn't know when I would see her again, but as Thunder said, I trusted June and Mike and knew Mother, and I would be together again soon.

Chapter Twelve

Homecoming

Summer was over, and the leaves on the trees had changed colors and were started to lose their leaves. Thunder told me this season is called fall, and the temperature will soon be turning wet and cold. Today June and Mike were late coming to the barn. It had been several months since Mother was taken away, and I still thought of her and hoped she was OK.

Several other humans were hanging out in front of my stall. Then I overheard them talking. "Mike and June are picking up Stormy from Broken Arrow Farm." My heart started to race. Then I saw the same truck and trailer that had taken Mother away coming down the road. In no time, it was backing up to the end of the barn. June was first out of the truck, raced to the back of the trailer, and opened the door. She jumped in; the next thing I saw was June leading Mother out. I let out a loud whinny. Mother saw me, replied with an even more piercing whinny, and tried to pull June to my stall. Instead, she opened the door to a stall next to me and put Mother into it. "Stormy, this is going to be your new home," she said. "Spirit is next to you with Thunder on the other side of him." She said, "all three of you will be together." "We will be just one big happy family." I was so happy we were all together just like it should be.

Mother let out another whinny as to approve of the accommodations, looked at a pile of hay in the corner, and proceeded to eat.

Chapter Thirteen

Saddle UP

Over the years, Mother and I had been on many exciting trail rides. She taught me many things about the herd and life.

Today, Mother said, would be an extraordinary day; it would be my last rite of passage to becoming a horse. I remember it like it was yesterday. I had just turned three, and it was the middle of August. It rained that morning, so there weren't any trail rides going out yet. Around midday, the sun came out, and there was a slight wind that helped dry out the grounds around the arena and the round pen. Many of the humans were hanging out inside the barn. They sang and had a good time. Soon June and Mike arrived and joined in.

I could hear them talking to the others about getting one of the pony saddles and who would be the brave soul or was that stupid to try and ride him. Then June asked Mike if his insurance was paid up. Not sure what all this meant at first, but I would soon find out.

June came into my stall and told me how much fun we would have. First, she put my halter on and brushed me from my face to the base of my tail. She brushed the area where my front leg met my chest. It seemed like she spent a lot of time in this area. She said that was where the girth would be, so she wanted to make sure I would not get any sores there.

Mike showed up with a small saddle that I had never seen before. June asked where it came from, and he told her, "It was an old pony saddle that belonged to the barn; it used to be used on Goldie." He said we should use the girth that is used on Stormy. It's perfect and shouldn't pull the hair or give him a saddle sore. I asked Mother what a saddle sore is, and she told me, "It's a kind of burn made by the girth rubbing the hair in the wrong direction, and it really hurts."

I was still very nervous, but I was confident that my owners would not do anything to hurt me. First, June took a saddle blanket hanging on the stall wall and rubbed it all over me. It had the scent of horses, and it felt kind of nice. When she draped it over my back, I flinched and wasn't sure I liked how it felt on my back, so I started to get restless and began to move around in the stall. The blanket then slid off my back onto the floor of the stall.   June picked it up, brushed it off, and put it on my back.

She then reached over to the stall wall again, picked up the saddle hanging there, and gently placed it on top of the blanket on my back. I had seen her do this many times to mother, so this didn't seem so bad; at least that's what I was thinking for the next couple of minutes.

I could feel the girth swinging under my stomach, then June quickly picked it up and started to tighten it, and I didn't like that. Then before I knew it, she unbuckled the saddle and quickly removed both the saddle and blanket. She handed them to Mike.

She led me out of my stall and up the hill to the round pen. I've seen many of my stable mates being trained there. Mike was coming up behind us, carrying the saddle and blanket. When we got to the gate, we stopped, and he went in front of us and opened it. June and I went in. Mike then closed the gate, and I could hear the click of the chain as he locked the gate. Then we started all over again with the blanket and saddle getting me used to the feel of them.

This time when she tightened the girth, she pulled it. At first, I held my breath, making my stomach push out so the girth wouldn't be so tight. Then after June had me walk around for a while, I started to breathe again. We then stopped, and she tightened the girth again. This time the girth was tight.

June was standing in the center of the pen. She pushed me away and used a piece of rope to get me to move around the sides of the round pen. At first, I was walking, but she flicked the rope towards my butt, and I started to trot. Then she would toss the rope in front of me so I would stop. Another flick of the rope towards my hind end, and I would change direction and trot again. When I would stop and try to walk closer to her, she would use the rope again to get me to move away and the direction she wanted me to go. I thought this wasn't so bad except for that darn saddle on my back. After a few minutes of trotting in one direction, I decided this started to feel more like work. Finally, I got the idea she was trying to show me who the boss was. After that, She dropped the rope to the ground, and I was allowed to walk up to her. Boy, I was glad that was over, I thought.

June then grabbed hold of my halter with one hand. Then I saw Mike reach over to the gate, pick up a bridle, and hand it to her. Mother had told me what a bridle was a long time ago, so I was familiar with its purpose. In a quick motion, she took the bridle, slipped the headpiece over my head, and placed my left ears through it, then my right ear. She then adjusted the brow band and buckled the throat latch. Then she slid the reins over my head and rested them on my neck. June told me, "this bridle is called a Hackamore; later, we will try a different bridle with a bit on it. For now, this will work. It belongs to your mother, Stormy." She then snapped the lead rope to the Hackamore.

Then Mike walked over from where he was standing. I could sense he was incredibly nervous. His scent was the same as after the first time he tried to trim my hooves. He was standing on my left side; first, he put one foot in the stirrup, then grabbed the saddle horn and started to pull himself up. He lifted his right leg and started to swing it over the saddle when the girth strap on the saddle broke.

The saddle rolled to my side; Mike came crashing down on the ground. The saddle then rolled off my back and around my side and stopped under my belly; I freaked. The billet strap was preventing the saddle from falling off of me. I started to kick and run, but June held tight to my lead rope.

Mike jumped to his feet, reached out, and grabbed for the billet strap. He pulled up on it and unfastened it. The saddle and blanket tumbled off my belly and landed with a thud on the ground. June could not hold me anymore, and she had to let go of the lead rope. I was running and bucking around the round pen for several minutes. Finally, Mike hobbled over toward me; he held his butt, and I could tell he was in pain. With a soothing voice, he was telling me everything was OK, and I needed to settle down. I could tell June was upset with what happened, and she was worried about Mike and me. I finally calmed down, and Mike walked over to me, reached out, and grabbed my lead rope. He led me over to June, who started to cry and put her arms around my neck. She kept telling me I was her baby and that everything would be OK. Boy, was I glad that was over? I thought it was time to go back to the barn - wrong.

June started to have me walk around the pen while Mike was walking back to the barn. After a few minutes, I could see him coming back up the hill with another saddle. In no time, he was back in pen with the new saddle. June asked him who it belonged to. He told her it was brand new Gini had just got it. One of the borders had bought it and didn't like it, so Gini purchased it. It is called a

Wintec, and it's exceptionally light, and I think it would be great for Spirit. He put it on one of the boards of the round pen. Then picked up the pony saddle and put it next to the new Wintec. Removed the girth and hooked it up to the new saddle.

He picked up the blanket brushed the leaves and dirt off it. Then he quickly put the saddle blanket back on my back. Picking up the new saddle, he put it on top of the blanket. The girth was swinging under my belly. I started to move around, but he grabbed one of the reins and told me it was OK. Then he reached under my belly, pulled the girth strap, put it through the D ring, and tightened it. Pulling up on the strap quickly, I didn't even have time to hold my breath.

June came over and was holding me while Mike started all over again. He then put his left foot in the stirrup and grabbed the saddle horn. He then pulled himself up. This time he just lay on the saddle putting his weight on my back for a short time. I had to shuffle my feet to adjust for this weight. Then he straightened up, swung his right leg over the saddle, and sat down on it. His right boot slid into the stirrup. Boy, he sure was heavy. June was still holding on to the lead rope and started to walk me around. I didn't like the weight on my back, but it was strange that I felt even more of a bond with both June and Mike. I see why my Mother and Thunder have such affection for them and a feeling of loyalty and wanting to please.

Mother was right; I was finally ready to fully join the herd and be an essential part of the barn.

Helping with the trail rides and someday working with young humans on learning to ride.

Chapter Fourteen

The Rodeo Parade

The humans in the barn had been talking about a parade for several weeks, and they wanted the barn to participate and take several of the horses. This would be an excellent chance to advertise the barn. Today I could hear Gini and June talking. They said they were making costumes to wear and wanted to decorate the horses. They were also talking about which horses would go to the parade. Gini said, "the barns horse trailer could only handle six horses."

My ears perked up when I heard my name mentioned, but Gini and June agreed I was too young. I was so disappointed, but I wasn't sure what a parade was anyway. Then Gini said they wanted to take the horse buggy, and several of the barn's young students could ride in the buggy and toss out candy. Sandy would pull the wagon. Everyone agreed that was a good idea. Mother's name was mentioned, but June was worried that she was not ready. She doesn't like to get in trailers. Mike then spoke and told them Thunder would be good and help support Stormy.

She finally agreed. Then they all agree Nikki, Cowboy, and Apache would be the final three, making a total of six. Rocky would be the reserve horse if my mother would not get on the trailer.

Several weeks had gone by, and several humans arrived at the barn early this morning. The barn was buzzing with humans running up and down from stall to stall in a short time. Both Mike and June were part of the first group of humans. Mother and Thunder were taken out of their stalls and moved to the washing area for a bath. They were then taken back into their stalls and brushed down their manes were combed. Their coats were shining, and their manes were just beautiful. Even their feet had been painted with black polish. I heard Mike say, "both of them looked like a Million Bucks'"

Soon I saw Mike back one of the horse trailers up to the barn. Nikki was the first to be led out of the barn and loaded into the trailer. Following her was Sandy, followed by Cowboy, then Apache. Mike and June were in Mother's stall discussing if they should load her or Thunder next. Finally, Gini suggested loading Stormy since she would probably be the hardest to get in the trailer. For mother, she hated trailers, and it was one of the hardest things she had to do.

Mother was let out of her stall, and down the center of the stable several of the humans were waiting around the trailer's opening to help if there was a problem. June walked her in several tight circles around the entrance to the trailer. Mother looked and saw everyone already loaded and standing quietly. To everyone's amazement, mother put one hoof onto the end of the trailer, then the other hoof, and in no time, she walked right into the trailer. All the humans were talking that this was the first time Mother had loaded onto a trailer without a fight.

Last but not least was Thunder; I had always heard Mike brag about how easy he was to load on a trailer. The horse trailer was very crowded with five horses already on it. It was a 6-horse trailer, but because Cowboy and Gideon were so large, that only left a small area at the end of the trailer. Mike tossed the lead rope around Thunder's neck, pointed his hand to the back of the trailer, and told Thunder to get in. Thunder glanced at Mike, looking back to the trailer, walked in, and turned sideways. I saw Mike and June jump into the pickup cab and drive off to the parade.

Several other humans got into their vehicles and followed them.

After the trailer was gone, one of the humans I had seen before returned to let us out into the big pasture.

After several hours I saw the trailer and several cars coming up the dirt road. Many of us whinnied to welcome them home, and we came running up to the gate. June was the first out and ran around to the back of the trailer and swung open the gate. Thunder again was the last one in the back, so first out, she grabbed ahold of his lead rope and walked I'm off the trailer. By that time, Mike met up with her, she gave him the rope, and he walked him to his stall. Then June reaches for mother's lead role. Mother swung around in the trailer so quickly it caught her by surprise. She then walked off the trailer and back to her stall. Other humans grabbed lead ropes, and the remaining horses were walked and put away in their stalls.

Mike and June were standing in front of my stall talking about the parade. I could tell they were extremely excited by their tone, and the parade went very well. Mike was telling everyone, "How proud he was of Thunder. At first, we carried An American flag. In the past, Thunder had always been afraid of waving flags". Mike had been working with him on overcoming his fear of waving flags. Mike said he did awesome with the flag, and then there was a problem with Sandy pulling the wagon. Sandy had horseshoes on that made her slide on the pavement, so we decided to use Thunder. We took his saddle off, put it into the back of the wagon, and hooked him up to the wagon. I'm pretty sure this was a first for him, and he did great."

June then started to talk about Mother. Loading on the trailer both at the barn and at the parade was monumental for her. At one point during the parade, the crowd started to come closer and closer on both sides of the road. This made the parade path so narrow and difficult to walk". She then started to get a slight quiver in her voice. She said, "Stormy suddenly stopped and started to walk to her left into the crowd. I tried to get her to turn back into the parade, but she wouldn't go. After going in the crowd about three or four people deep. Stormy stopped again. This time in front of her was a little girl in a wheelchair. Stormy then lowered her head so the little girl could pet her. The little girl's mother thanked me. I told her, "don't thank me; you can thank my horse. With so many people, I really didn't see your little girl". June said, "she was so proud of

Stormy." I could see her from my stall and saw tears streaming down her face as she was telling everyone what had happened.

I was also proud of my Mother. She has come so far, and June's bond is an incredibly special one.

Chapter Fifteen

The Big Move

It's late summer, the middle of the day, and the middle of the week. Much of the pasture had turned brown, burned by the summer heat and lack of rain. The farm was empty of humans. Mike and June usually showed up at the barn on the weekends. We had not been fed yet, so I'm sure we thought our owners would be coming to feed us soon. Looking out of my stall, I could see Mike's truck coming down the winding drive to the barn. Behind his truck was a different horse trailer I had not seen before. It was long and the same color as Mike's truck, a bright red.

June got out of the truck first and went straight to mother's stall. She picked up her tackle box from the stall wall; then, on to Thunder's stall, she got his box and put them into the back of the pickup truck. The tackle boxes were full of multiple items like our brushes and hoof picks. Mike had both saddles, one over each arm placing them in the back of the truck. He yelled out to June that he would get the horse blankets. June was in Mother's stall telling her something about needing her to be a big good girl and doing something she knew mother did not like to do. That is, she needed her to get into the trailer as fast as possible. Stormy, June said, "I promise you where you guys are going is wonderful. It has a lush pasture, lots of water and it's going be a great new home for all of us".

The rest of the supplies were loaded into the truck. They also loaded some bags of feed, water buckets, all the extra halters, horse blankets, bridles. Then she put halters on Mother and me. Then Mike put Thunders halter on him. Mike told her, "It might be a good idea to put me in first since I had never been on a trailer before. With Spirit on the trailer, Stormy would probably go peacefully".

June came into my stall and attached the lead rope to my halter. She led me out of my stall toward the trailer. When I got closer to the door, Mike opened the back end. I didn't like the looks of this. I started to back up, pulling against the rope. June began to talk to me with her usual soothing voice, explaining where we were going. I calmed down, putting one front hoof on the wooden bed of the trailer. It felt solid and hard, so I put my second front hoof on it, stretching my body out to prevent the back legs from going in. I felt the gentle tug on the lead rope and eventually walked into the trailer. She led me to the front of the trailer

75

and tied the rope to a hook on the sidewall. Mike closed the gate, dividing the trailer into two compartments: a front and a back. With the lead rope tied and the gate closed, I couldn't back up. I started to panic but quickly settled down.

I saw Mike and June look at each other and smile. she said, "that was easy; hopefully Stormy will do the same thing? June then went back to the barn for Mother. I was watching through the slats of the trailer when I saw the two of them coming closer. I started to whinny because I wanted Mother to be with me: her ears perked up. She responded to whinny back to me. Mike opened the back of the trailer, and Mother didn't even hesitate; she walked straight onto the trailer. Mike swung open the dividing gate, and June put Mother next to me. She tied her lead rope to the inside trailer post. Mike closed the gate behind us and locked it. June opened the side door and walked out.

Mother told me Mike was walking Thunder out of his stall and coming toward the trailer. I couldn't see much because Mother was blocking my view, but I heard him tell Thunder to get on the trailer. Then the clip, clop of his hoofs on the floor of the trailer. Mike then shut the back door. I felt safe with all of us being together.

Mike told June to make one last trip through the stalls, and he would check the tack house to make sure they didn't forget anything. The next thing I remember was the truck doors opening and the engine coming alive. We started to move, and I almost lost my balance. I bumped into Mother, which stopped me from falling. After a few turns, I got the feel of shifting my weight to prevent falling.

Chapter Sixteen

Home Sweet Home

It seemed like we were traveling forever when we came to a stop and then made a right turn onto another driveway similar to the old barn entrance. This road was much shorter then we came to a halt. I heard the engine shut off. The truck doors opened, and both Mike and June got out and came around to the back door. It swung open, and Mike walked Thunder out and into this new pasture.

He told June to wait until he came back to get us out. After a few minutes, I saw him walking alongside the trailer toward the back and heard him inside it. Suddenly our gate opened. June came in through the side door, untied Mother, and slowly backed her out of the trailer. When they reached the end of the trailer, she turned around and walked out of the trailer. Mike then grabbed my halter and started to walk me out. When I reached the end of the trailer, I decided to take a giant leap to the ground. Mike was surprised and pulled on the lead rope to keep me under control. I was just having fun. He walked me around outside for a few minutes: then, we went through a gate. Mike unhooked my rope and told me, "welcome to your new home." I stood there for a few minutes saw both Mother and Thunder standing in the middle of the pasture eating away. I looked around, and June was right; it was a lovely place, and the field was knee-high in lush green grass.

Chapter Seventeen

A New Life

The original barn I was born in is long gone. I will never see my old friends: Cowboy, Apache, Gideon, Rocky, and several others. Even to this day, I wonder what they are doing. We had moved into a new barn that Mike and June had built. This pasture is still nicer than the old one. There are many new trails on it, and we have had countless hours of fun riding them.

I was so sad when Thunder passed away several years ago.

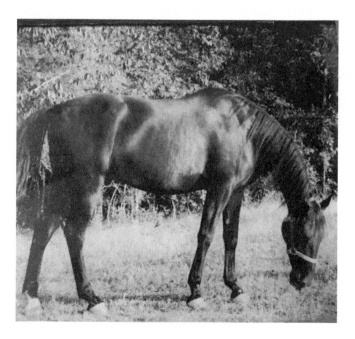

After that, Mike moved me into his stall and told me I was now the head of the herd. I felt very honored. I miss him: his stories and wisdom so much. He taught me many things, and I try to follow them to this day. Then Mother passed away. It was the saddest day in my life. I remember it like it was just yesterday. Often, June comes to my stall and puts her arms around my neck. She tells me how much she loves me and misses my Mother, and I am her baby.

Both are buried on the property by the edge of the driveway. I often go to the fence and stand looking at their grave and talk to both of them. New horses have been added to the herd, and I try to pass on the stories and wisdom given to me by my Mother and Thunder.

I love both June and Mike, and we have become very close through the years. A new young human has also been introduced into my life: his name is Seth. I feel a special connection with him. I am not sure what the future will hold for us, but I'm looking forward to it.

Several new horses have been added to the barn. My lifelong dream has come true. I am the Stallion of the barn

Mother, is this my good side? I could use more treats!

The End